Celebration Songs
for Keyboard

Music arranged and processed by Barnes Music Engraving Ltd
East Sussex TN22 4HA, UK

Cover design by xheight Limited

Published 1995

Anniversary Song

Words and Music by Al Jolson and Saul Chaplin

Suggested Registration: Strings
Rhythm: Waltz
Tempo: ♩ = 160

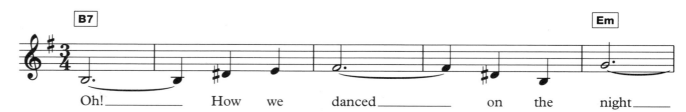

Oh!_____ How we danced_____ on the night_____

— we were wed,_____ we vowed_____ our true

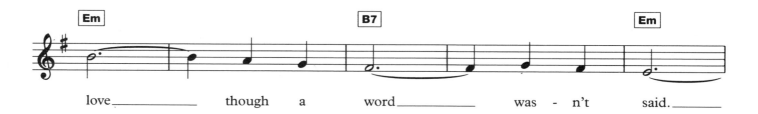

love_____ though a word_____ was-n't said._____

— The world_____ was in bloom,_____ there were

stars_____ in the skies,_____ ex-cept_____

— for the few_____ that were there_____ in your

Campbell Connelly & Co Ltd, London W1V 5TZ

THE ANNIVERSARY WALTZ

Words and Music by Al Dubin and Dave Franklin

Suggested Registration: Strings
Rhythm: Waltz
Tempo: ♩ = 124

Tell me I may al - ways have the

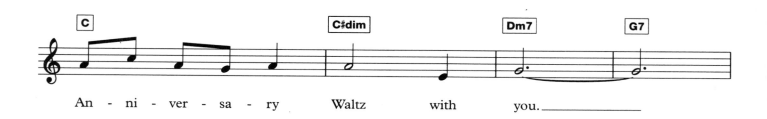

An - ni - ver - sa - ry Waltz with you._____

Tell me this is real ro - mance, an

an - ni - ver - sa - ry dream come true._____ Let

this be the an - them to our fu - ture years, to

mil - lions of smiles, and a few lit - tle tears.

May I al - ways lis - ten to the

An - ni - ver - sa - ry Waltz with you._____

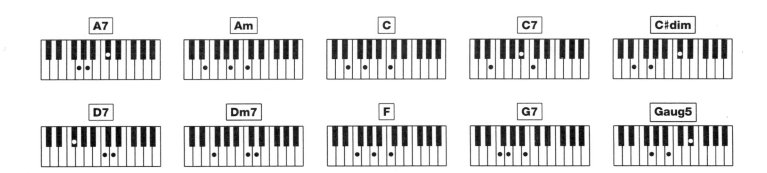

C'EST MAGNIFIQUE

12 5/6

Words and Music by Cole Porter

Suggested Registration: Vibraphone
Rhythm: Slow Swing
Tempo: ♩ = 124

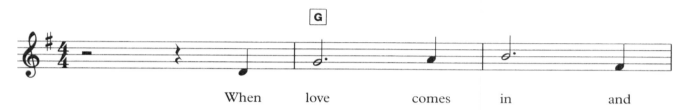

When love comes in and

takes you for a spin, ooh la la la, _____

c'est mag – ni – fi – que.   When

ev – ery night   your loved one holds you

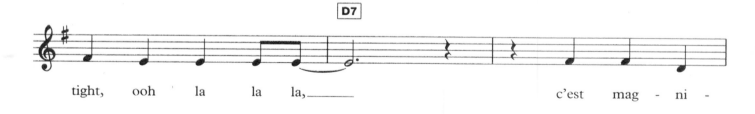

tight, ooh la la la, _____   c'est mag – ni –

– fi – que,   but when one

day   your   loved   one   drifts   a - way,   ooh   la   la   la,___

___   it   is   so   tra - gi - que,

but   when,   once   more,   she

whis - pers,   'Je   t'a - dore,'   c'est   mag - ni -

- fi -   que._____

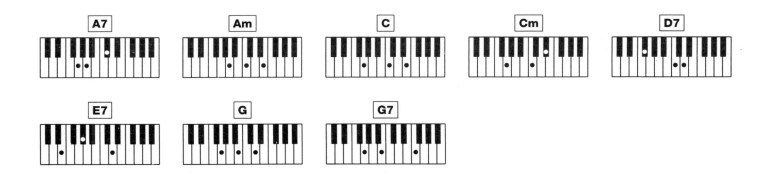

CELEBRATION

Words and Music by Ronald Bell, Claydes Smith, George Brown, James Tayler,
Robert Mickens, Earl Toon, Dennis Thomas, Robert Bell and Eumir Deodato

Suggested Registration: Jazz Organ
Rhythm: 16 Beat
Tempo: ♩ = 125

Ce - le - brate good times, come on.

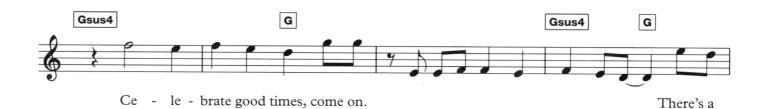

Ce - le - brate good times, come on. There's a

par - ty go -ing on right here, a ce - le - bra-tion to last through-out the

years, so bring your good times, and your laugh - ter too. __

We're gon' ce - le - brate your par - ty with you. __ Come on now, ce - le -

- bra - tion, __ let's all ce - le - brate and have a good time. __

Congratulations

Words and Music by Bill Martin and Phil Coulter

12 3+4

Suggested Registration: Clarinet
Rhythm: Swing
Tempo: ♩ = 180

11

FOR HE'S A JOLLY GOOD FELLOW

Traditional

Suggested Registration: Clarinet
Rhythm: 6/8 March
Tempo: ♩. = 104

For he's a jol - ly good fel - low, for

he's a jol - ly good fel - low, for he's a jol - ly good

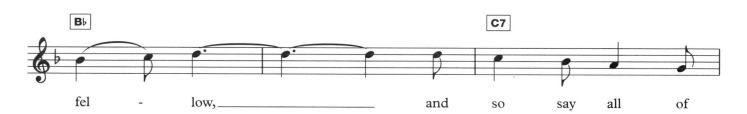

fel - low, _____ and so say all of

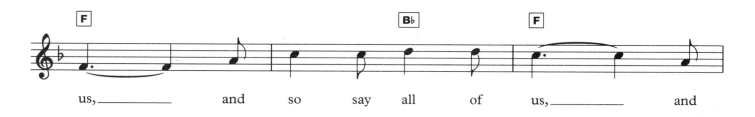

us, _____ and so say all of us, _____ and

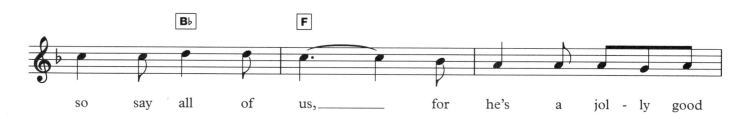

so say all of us, _____ for he's a jol - ly good

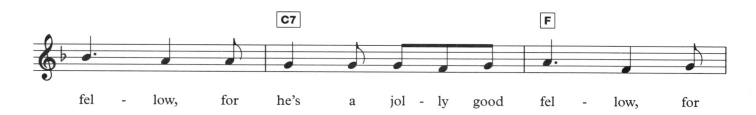

fel - low, for he's a jol - ly good fel - low, for

Happy Anniversary

Words and Music by Gary S Paxton

Suggested Registration: Acoustic Guitar
Rhythm: Slow Swing
Tempo: ♩ = 132

It's not get-ting old-er, just much bet-ter, you

bring me so much hap-pi-ness each day.

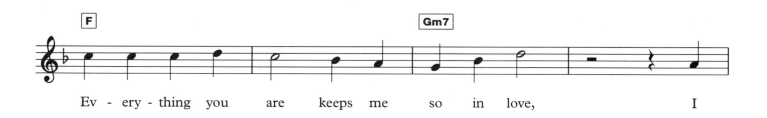

Ev-ery-thing you are keeps me so in love, I

thank the hea-vens that you came my way. And

dar - ling, hap - py an - ni - ver - sa - ry,_____ an -

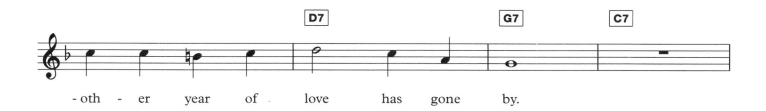

-oth - er year of love has gone by.

Thank you for each day you give to me,_____ my

dar - ling hap - py an - ni - ver - sa - ry._____

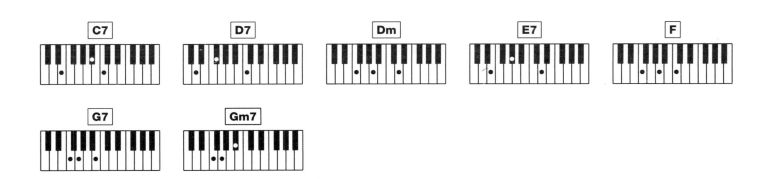

Happy Birthday Sweet Sixteen

Words and Music by Neil Sedaka and Howard Greenfield

Suggested Registration: Piano
Rhythm: 8 Beat
Tempo: ♩ = 150

Tra la la la la la___ la la la, hap-py birth-day sweet six - teen.___

Tra la la la la la___ la la la, hap-py birth-day sweet six - teen.___

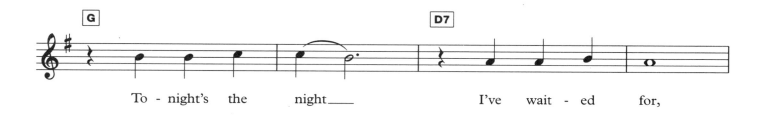

To - night's the night___ I've wait - ed for,

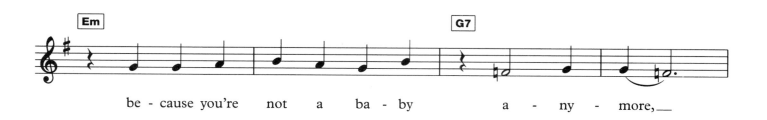

be - cause you're not a ba - by a - ny - more,___

you've turned in - to the pret - ti-est girl I've ev - er seen,___

Happy Birthday To You

Words and Music by Patty S Hill and Mildred Hill

Suggested Registration: French Horn
Rhythm: Waltz
Tempo: ♩ = 88-110

Hap - py birth - day to you, hap - py birth - day to

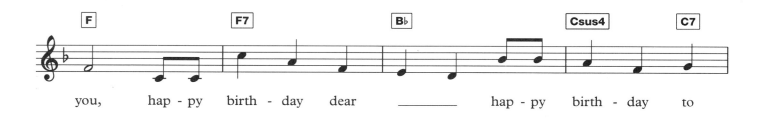

you, hap - py birth - day dear _____ hap - py birth - day to

you. From good friends and true, from old friends and

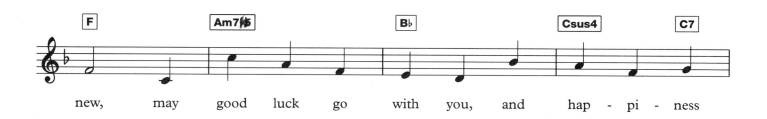

new, may good luck go with you, and hap - pi - ness

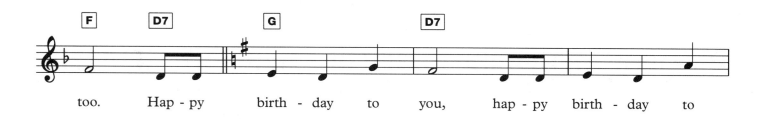

too. Hap - py birth - day to you, hap - py birth - day to

19

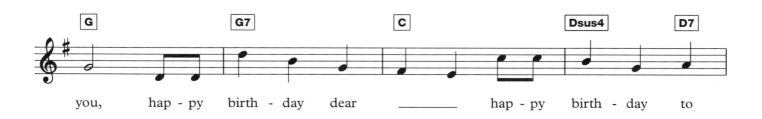

you, hap - py birth - day dear _____ hap - py birth - day to

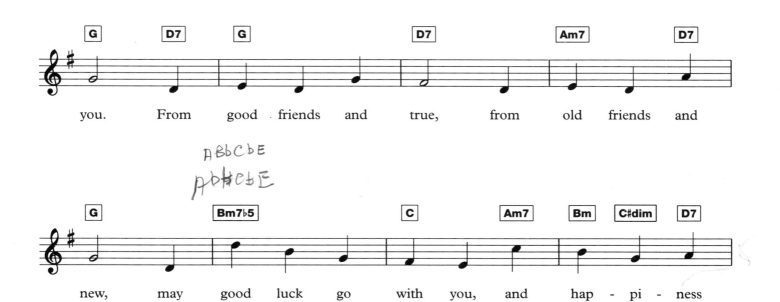

you. From good friends and true, from old friends and

A♭♭C♭E
A♭♯C♭E

new, may good luck go with you, and hap - pi - ness

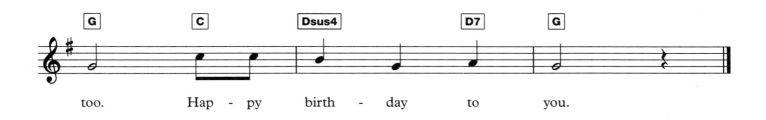

too. Hap - py birth - day to you.

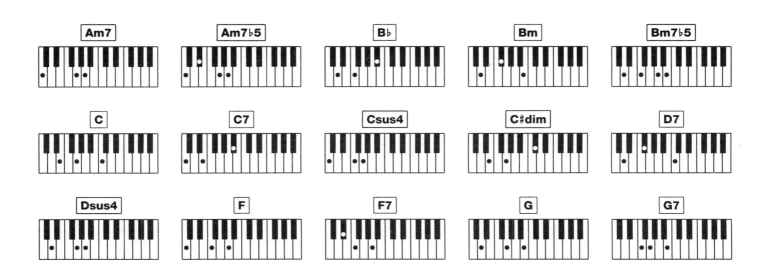

Happy Holiday

Words and Music by Irving Berlin

Suggested Registration: Vibraphone
Rhythm: Slow Swing
Tempo: ♩ = 94

I'M SITTING ON TOP OF THE WORLD

Words by Sam Lewis and Joe Young / Music by Ray Henderson

Suggested Registration: Piano
Rhythm: Swing
Tempo: ♩ = 172

I'm Twenty One Today

Words and Music by Alec Kendal

Suggested Registration: Clarinet
Rhythm: March 6/8
Tempo: ♩ = 100

I'm twen - ty-one to-day,

twen - ty-one to-day, I've got the key of the door, ne-ver been twen - ty-one be-fore, and

Pa says I can do as I like so shout, 'Hip, hip, hoo-ray!

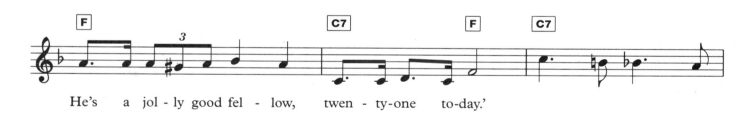

He's a jol-ly good fel-low, twen-ty-one to-day.'

I'm twen - ty-one to-day, twen-ty-one to-day,

I've got the key of the door, ne-ver been twen-ty-one be-fore, and

It's A Hap Hap Happy Day

Words by Al Neiburg / Music by Sammy Timberg and Winston S Sharples

Suggested Registration: Clarinet
Rhythm: Swing
Tempo: ♩ = 124

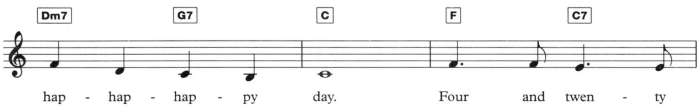

Let The Good Times Roll

Words and Music by Leonard Lee

Suggested Registration: Saxophone
Rhythm: Shuffle
Tempo: ♩ = 120

Come on ba-by, let the good times roll,___ come on ba-by, let me

thrill your soul,___ come on___ ba-by, let the good times roll,_____

roll on and on._____ Come on ba-by, let me

hold you tight,___ tell me ev-ery-thing is right to-night.___

Come on___ ba-by, let the good times roll,_____ roll___ on and

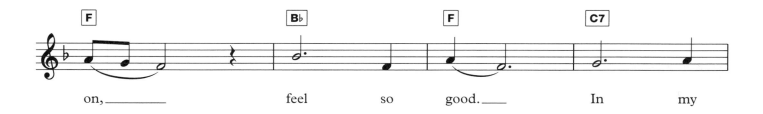

on,_____ feel so good.____ In my

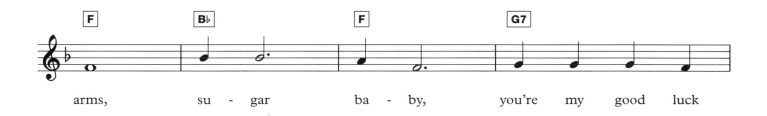

arms, su - gar ba - by, you're my good luck

charm. Come on ba - by, let the good times roll,___

come on ba - by, let me thrill your soul,_ come on___ ba - by, let the

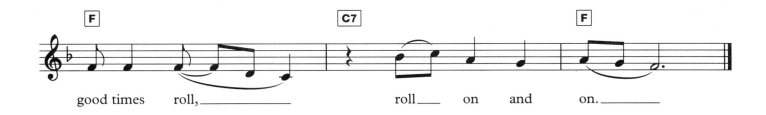

good times roll,_____ roll___ on and on._____

Oh Happy Day

Words and Music by Edwin R Hawkins

Suggested Registration: Jazz Organ
Rhythm: Rhythm & Blues
Tempo: ♩ = 116

Oh hap-py day, ____ oh hap-py day, _____

when Je - sus washed, _ oh when he washed, _____

when Je - sus washed, _ he washed my sins __ a - way.

__ (Oh hap-py day) ____ Oh hap-py day. ____ (Oh hap-py day)

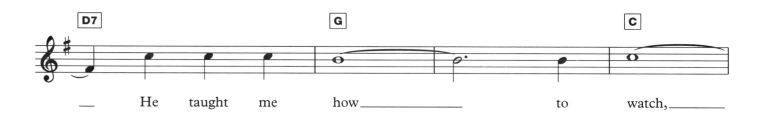

__ He taught me how _____ to watch, _____

31

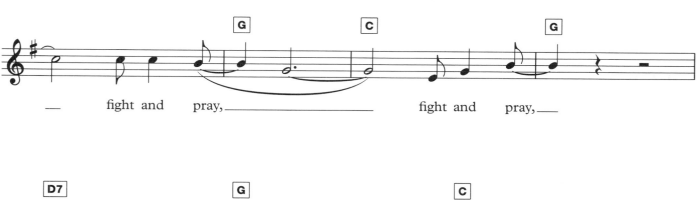

fight and pray,_____ fight and pray,___

and live re - joic - ing ev - ery day,

_____ ev - ery day.___ Oh hap - py day,

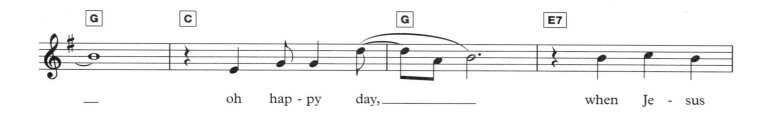

___ oh hap - py day,_____ when Je - sus

washed, he washed my sins__ a - way._____

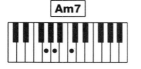
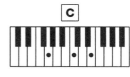

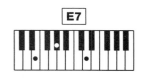
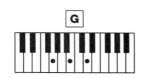

OH, WHAT A BEAUTIFUL MORNIN'

Words by Oscar Hammerstein II / Music by Richard Rodgers

Suggested Registration: French Horn
Rhythm: Waltz
Tempo: ♩ = 156

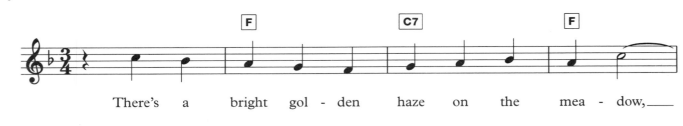

There's a bright gol - den haze on the mea - dow,___

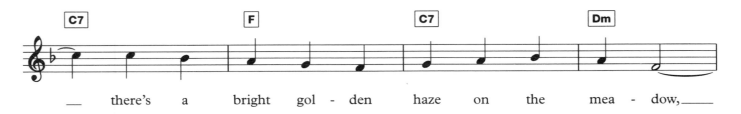

___ there's a bright gol - den haze on the mea - dow,___

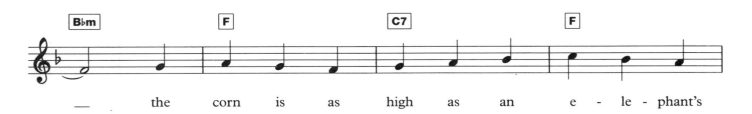

___ the corn is as high as an e - le - phant's

eye, an' it looks like it's climb - in' clear up to the

sky. Oh, what a beau - ti - ful morn -

- in', oh, what a beau - ti - ful day,___

33

SPRING, SPRING, SPRING!

Words by Johnny Mercer / Music by Gene De Paul

II 142

Suggested Registration: Vibraphone
Rhythm: Slow Swing
Tempo: ♩ = 104

Oh, the barn - yard is bu - sy, in a re - gu - lar tiz - zy, and the

ob - vi - ous rea - son is be - cause of the sea - son. Ma Na - ture's ly - ri - cal with

her year - ly mi - ra - cle, Spring, Spring, Spring! All the

hen folk are watch - in' while their men folk are scratch - in' to en - sure the sur - vi - val of each

brand new ar - ri - val. Each nest is twit - ter - ing, they're all ba - by sit - ter - ing, it's

Spring, Spring, Spring! It's a bee - hive of bud - ding son and

STRIKE UP THE BAND

Music and Lyrics by George Gershwin and Ira Gershwin

Suggested Registration: Clarinet
Rhythm: Slow Swing
Tempo: ♩ = 144

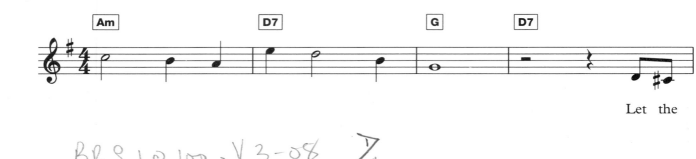

Let the

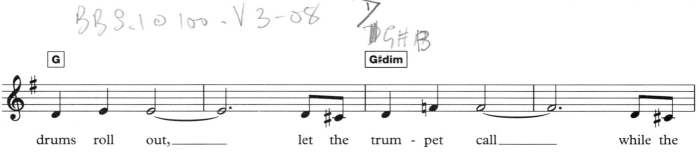

drums roll out,_____ let the trum - pet call_____ while the

peo - ple shout,_____ 'Strike up the band!'_____ Hear the

cym - bals ring,_____ call - ing one and all_____ to that

hap - py swing,_____ strike up the band._____ Yan - kee

Doo doo - dle - oo, doo - dle - oo, we'll come through, doo - dle - oo, doo - dle -

- oo, for the red, white and blue, doo - dle - oo, lend a hand._____

_____ With the flag un - furled,_____ we can face the world,_____

hey, lead - er, strike up the band!_____

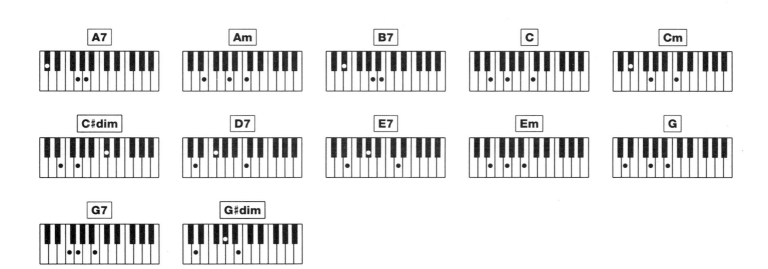

Walking On Sunshine

Words and Music by Kimberley Rew

Suggested Registration: Saxophone
Rhythm: 8 Beat (double time feel)
Tempo: ♩ = 104

We Are The Champions

Words and Music by Freddie Mercury

Suggested Registration: Electric Guitar
Rhythm: 6/8 Slow Rock
Tempo: ♩. = 63

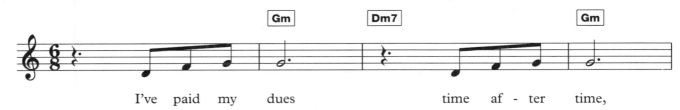

I've paid my dues time af - ter time,

I've done my____ sen - tence, but com - mit - ted no crime,

and bad mis - takes, I've made a few,

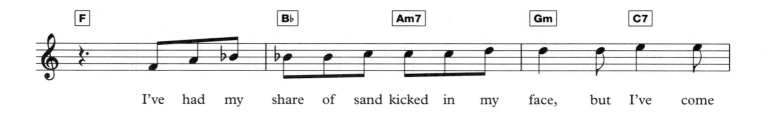

I've had my share of sand kicked in my face, but I've come

through. We____ are the

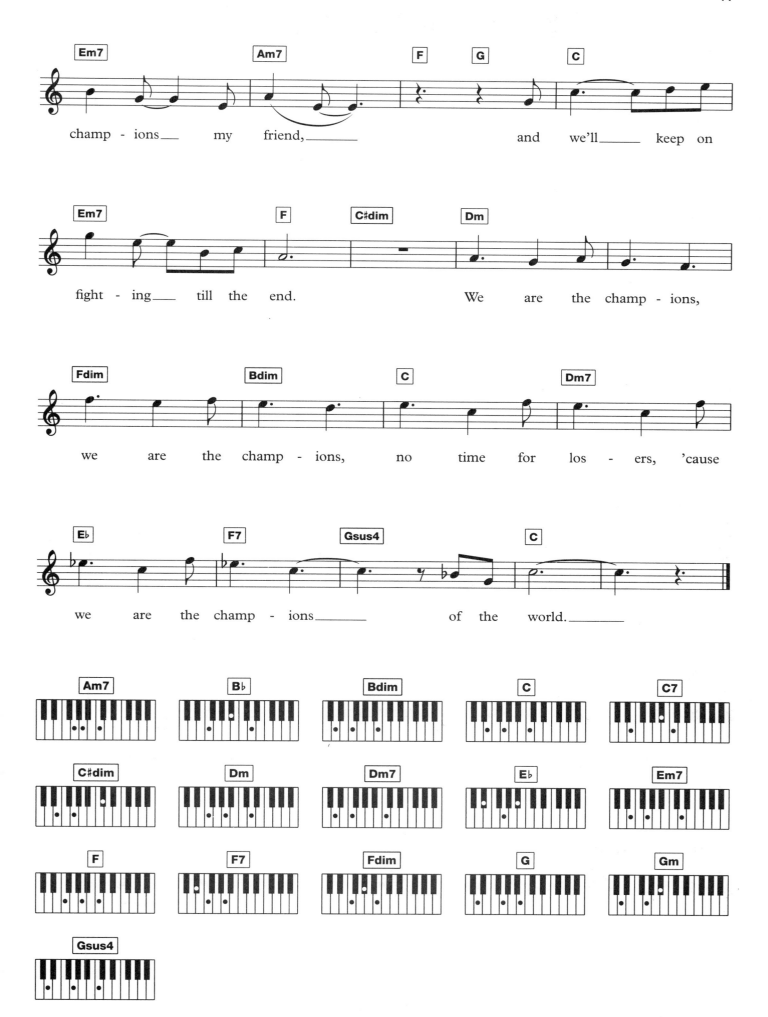

We're In The Money

Words by Al Dubin / Music by Harry Warren

Suggested Registration: Piano
Rhythm: Swing
Tempo: ♩ = 160

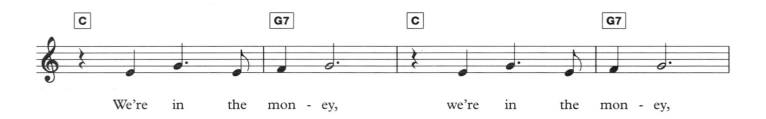

We're in the mon - ey, we're in the mon - ey,

we've got a lot of what it takes to get a - long.

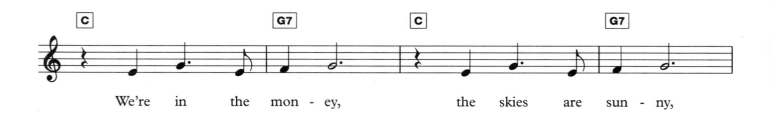

We're in the mon - ey, the skies are sun - ny,

Old Man De - pres - sion, you are through, you done us wrong.

A Wonderful Day Like Today

Words and Music by Leslie Bricusse and Anthony Newley

Suggested Registration: Clarinet
Rhythm: Swing
Tempo: ♩ = 184

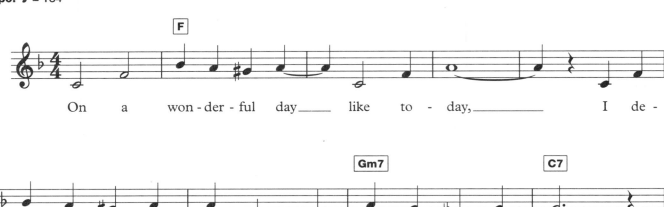

On a won-der-ful day___ like to-day,___ I de-

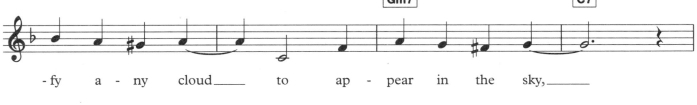

-fy a-ny cloud___ to ap-pear in the sky,___

dare a-ny rain-drop to plop in my eye,___ on a won-der-ful day

___ like to- day. _____ On a morn-ing like this___

___ I could kiss ev-ery-bo-dy, I'm so full of love___ and good-

-will. _____ Let me say fur-ther-more,___ I'd a-

You're Sixteen, You're Beautiful (And You're Mine)

Words and Music by Robert Sherman and Richard Sherman

Suggested Registration: Saxophone
Rhythm: Shuffle
Tempo: ♩ = 116

You came on like a dream, peach-es and cream, lips like straw-ber-ry wine,___ you're six-teen,___ you're beau-ti-ful, and you're mine.___ You're all rib-bons and curls,_ ooh, what a girl,___ eyes that spar-kle and shine, _ you're six-teen,___ you're beau-ti-ful,___ and you're mine.

You're my ba - by,

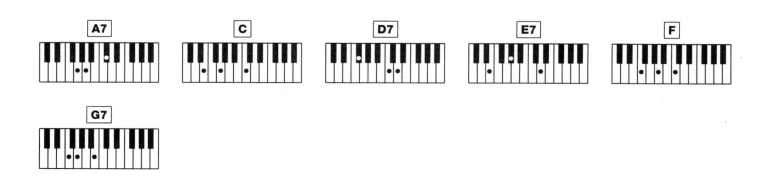

THE EASY KEYBOARD LIBRARY

Also available in the Decades Series

THE TWENTIES
including:

Ain't Misbehavin'
Ain't She Sweet?
Baby Face
The Man I Love

My Blue Heaven
Side By Side
Spread A Little Happiness
When You're Smiling

THE THIRTIES
including:

All Of Me
A Fine Romance
I Wanna Be Loved By You
I've Got You Under My Skin

The Lady Is A Tramp
Smoke Gets In Your Eyes
Summertime
Walkin' My Baby Back Home

THE FORTIES
including:

Almost Like Being In Love
Don't Get Around Much Any More
How High The Moon
Let There Be Love

Sentimental Journey
Swinging On A Star
Tenderly
You Make Me Feel So Young

THE FIFTIES
including:

All The Way
Cry Me A River
Dream Lover
High Hopes

Magic Moments
Mister Sandman
A Teenager In Love
Whatever Will Be Will Be

THE SIXTIES
including:

Cabaret
Happy Birthday Sweet Sixteen
I'm A Believer
The Loco-motion

My Kind Of Girl
Needles And Pins
There's A Kind Of Hush
Walk On By

THE SEVENTIES
including:

Chanson D'Amour
Hi Ho Silver Lining
I'm Not In Love
Isn't She Lovely

Save Your Kisses For Me
Take Good Care Of My Baby
We've Only Just Begun
You Light Up My Life

THE EIGHTIES
including:

Anything For You
China In Your Hand
Everytime You Go Away
Golden Brown

I Want To Break Free
Karma Chameleon
Nikita
Take My Breath Away

THE NINETIES
including:

Crocodile Shoes
I Swear
A Million Love Songs
The One And Only

Promise Me
Sacrifice
Think Twice
Would I Lie To You?